LAUGHTER IS THE
BREAST MEDICINE

An Inspirational
Book of Humor

love, love & laugh

Eileen Kaplan

EILEEN KAPLAN

EyeKap Press
eyekap@att.net

Printed in the United States of America

ISBN-10:   0-615-30411-7
ISBN-13: 978-0-615-30411-3

Library of Congress Control Number: 2009906335

Cover and book design by Shoshanah Siegel

Illustrations by Kraig Sanquedolce

To order: laughteristhebreastmedicine.com

To my husband Arney,
who has always been
"the wind beneath my wings".

"Chemo is a form of therapy...so is laughter."

Eileen Kaplan

Legends say that the hummingbirds float free of time, carrying our hopes for love, joy and celebration. The hummingbird's delicate grace reminds us that life is rich, beauty is everywhere, every personal connection has meaning and that laughter is life's sweetest creation.© *Papyrus Greeting Cards*

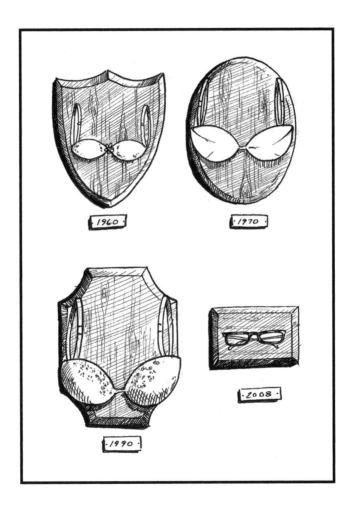

Laugh at...

LAUGHTER IS THE BREAST MEDICINE

Stand Up and Salute

Once upon a time there were two itsy, bitsy breast buds.
These baby buds were first measured (naked) by "The Bra
Lady" at an upscale department store. I was only ten years old.
G-d, how embarrassing!

They were perky A-minus buds. My "Beginners Bra" took its
bow.

I have vivid memories of practicing for hours on end, with
my arms behind my back, trying to hook my bra. To turn the
bra around and hook it in the front was not the solution for
this determined kid. And being as stubborn as I am, it was the
hard way or no way. Finally, success at sunset.

Back to my buds. These two little buds were coaxed and
coddled by the trainer bra, the longline strapless bras, the
pushup bras, the wonderful bra, and even the all day bra.

And let's not forget the foam cups, G-d forbid you showed your nipples. My girlfriend Kim and I laughingly called them the nipless bras.

In my later years, I wore underwire bras and, then, finally the minimizers. Well, what do you know? I actually tried to make my breasts look smaller.

My two little buds grew up and became two beautiful C-cup breasts, lovingly admired by my boyfriend, who, thankfully, became my husband.

My breasts took on a life of their own. A cyst here and there, stretch marks from the pregnancies that brought us our two beautiful girls, a bump appearing and disappearing.

One day, my breasts decided to have breast cancer.

There are so many different breast cancer diagnoses, so many emotions, so many prognoses, and so many treatments created to kill the uninvited guests that have decided to set up house-keeping in our breasts. And, then, there was treatment designed expressly for my own breasts.

Gee, could I actually have Designer Breasts? This was a positive.

While I know that breast cancer is not a laughing matter, I chose to keep my brain above my boobs, stay as positive as I could, and try to make a funny out of everything and anything.

I was determined to make laughter my mantra.

Coincidentally, I happened to be reading my decades-old high school yearbook just prior to my cancer diagnosis. Inscribed under my class picture were the words:

"She shall have laughter wherever she goes."

I hope you'll relax and have a chuckle as you join me on my breast cancer adventure. You might also see yourself or someone you love in this personal, yet universal, adventure.

Above all, remember...*Laughter Is The Breast Medicine*!

KNOW THOSE BOOBIES
...And Really Feel Yourself Up

Everyone needs a "breast buddy." Believe it or not, my breast buddy is my husband's best friend.

How did this happen? One day, many pre-cancer years ago, my husband and our longtime buddy, Kenny, went fishing and afterward, because he had to go directly to a business meeting, Kenny showered and changed into fresh clothes at our home.

Kenny came out of the bathroom, and hanging on his jacket pocket was my shower breast examination instruction tab.

We all laughed our butts off! And so, from that day on, the first of every month, Kenny would call me (he never missed a month) and say, "Eileen, have you checked your breasts today?"

Our friend, my "breast buddy," Kenny, was instrumental in saving my life. Thank you, Kenny, from the bottom of my heart for being so nutty!

Soaping up and singing in the shower, I lathered up my boobs religiously every month. It's a lot easier to feel those party-crashers lurking when your boobs are slippery.

Doing those circles in the shower, I felt something very unusual in my right boob. I felt it again. It was popping under my soapy, slippery fingers.

My brain was screaming, "Tumor, tumor!" I knew it immediately.

While the bells and whistles went off in my brain, I began to give myself mental instructions: "Eileen, call your primary care physician."

When I called, the receptionist said, "Well, you have a regular appointment next week, and it probably can wait until then."

I knew it couldn't.

Immediately, I called my gynecologist's office. When I told the staff about the uninvited guest I'd found, the girls, whom I've known for years, started screaming, "Come in first thing tomorrow."

And so, the curtain opened, and the wild adventure began.

BOOBOLOGY 101

What is the definition of an *eternity*?

Holding your breath during the mammogram.

Then waiting for a sign from above.

"I have to take a few more pictures," the X-ray tech said in a concerned voice.

Years ago, I'd been an X-ray technician, so I knew what that meant, and it made me very suspicious.

And there's nothing like being subjected to more mammo pain when I know there's an uninvited guest in my right boob that's going to be squeezed again. I'm thinking an MRI, a

Pet Scan (do they X-ray your pets, too?), and a CT Scan (also called a CAT Scan. No, they don't X-ray your cats), even a biopsy sounds great. But do they really think that soft pads on the mammography machine are going to reduce the pain of a boob being squished? NO!

I wasn't nervous, I just wanted them to lay the news on me so I could get on with my life.

I got the call from my gynecologist.

"Eileen, you have DCIS. This is Ductal Carcinoma in Situ."

I knew that Ductal means duct, and Carcinoma means cancer, but what the heck is in Situ? The doctor explained that carcinoma in situ is a malignant tumor in the premetastatic stage, which means that it's encapsulated and has not escaped from the mammary duct. What luck!

I met my surgeon and, boy, oh boy was he handsome. As he explained all the wonderful choices I had to get rid of the uninvited guest, I knew that he was talking to me to take my mind off him feeling up my boobs.

My husband, who was watching the sideshow said, "You know, doctor, you're the first guy I ever had to pay such a high price to, to feel up my wife's breasts!" My handsome doctor smiled and blushed. We all laughed. The ice was broken. This was good.

I'd have the uninvited guest removed. My handsome surgeon would do a lumpectomy.

My Coming Out Party

First, I had a biopsy.

During the biopsy, a teeny, weeny marker is deposited at the site of the party-crasher in my boob so the surgeon can go directly to it during the lumpectomy.

In getting this thing out of me, the surgeon would go out to the margins. It sounded like he was writing an English report, but the only one doing any writing was me—he'd asked me to write the word YES on my right breast.

A few nodes had to be removed under my arm so the uninvited guest had company going to the lab.

I asked my doctor, "How do you find those nodes?"

"Oh," the doctor said, "I inject a little psychedelic blue dye just above your nipple, and the dye travels to your nodes via your mammary ducts. The psychedelic blue dye lights up the sentinel node like a flashing neon sign."

Cut here on the dotted line!

On the day of reckoning, a lovely receptionist gave me a little snow glass that said, "Good Luck!" A good omen.

The anesthesiologist found a healthy vein, but the needle landed on a nerve in my wrist. Pain! "I'm fainting."

"Put her out!" the doctor yelled.

In and out of surgery, I hope he found the margins.

As I rested in recovery, my handsome doctor came in to check on me.

I said, "Doctor, could you just answer one question for me?"

"Yes," he answered.

"You know that I'm only 60 years old. Does that mean I won't be able to nurse anymore?"

Laughing, he promised me that the minute he had the news about the nodes he'd call me.

I was discharged to go home and w..a..i..t.

On Saturday, at 4 p.m. in the grocery store, my cell phone rang and my compassionate surgeon told me that I had negative nodes. Yippee! I began crying in glee in the potato chip aisle of the grocery store, shouting in a loud voice, "Hey, everyone, I have negative nodes, I have negative nodes!"

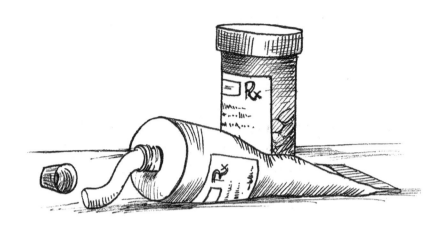

THE RASH

Something thick, ugly, and red was blossoming on my surgical area. I was allergic to the iodine in the surgical wash—you know, the stuff that's supposed to keep you from getting an infection.

My fabulous doctor inspected the rash, and ordered medicine for it and told me he'd see me in three days.

Three days later, I was in an examining room and wearing one of those crazy johnnies that open in the front.

My doctor walked in and said, "How are you doing?"

I flung open the johnnie and said, "Look at the clown!" I had red polka dots all over my entire body from head to toe.

All we could do was laugh.

"Well, I think maybe you should see a dermatologist," he said. No kidding. Good idea, Doc!

Thank G-d, my terrific dermatologist saw me immediately, ordered a stronger pill and a stronger ointment. It took three weeks for this ravishing rash to leave my body, and leave it did, right out through the tips of my toes, through the top of my head, and out through my fingertips. Amen.

Instant Hot Flashes

When I met my fabulous female oncologist, I thought, hooray! A woman at last. Petite and adorable, she's a wonderful, kind, take no nonsense woman. And she actually took the time to talk with me. For once, I was speechless!

With a gentle smile on her face, she told me that my uninvited guest was negative. This meant that it could only be attacked with a specific treatment and that her recipe for my treatment was four infusions of chemotherapy and 32 lightning rods of radiation therapy.

Will I lose my hair? Eyelashes? Eyebrows? Silly questions,

especially when I knew the answers. I'll be as bald as a
cue ball.

Whoever dreamed up chemotherapy must've been a torture
expert.

My oncologist said, "Don't worry, I won't let you get sick. I'll
mix up one of my famous pill cocktails to keep you from being
nauseous and throwing up."

For days after my chemo infusions, my outstanding oncologist called me to see how I was feeling, to check on the
anti-nausea cocktail, and to see if I was praying to the porcelain
G-d.

The only problem I was having was hiccupping and
swallowing. She decided to give me something to relax my
esophagus. Good thinking. I could eat again.

My Chemo Kit

My Chemo Kit started with my wonderful husband of many decades, lots of strength, and big, fat veins. If your veins are rolling and don't look like big fat blue worms, the nurse can't puncture them. So, out came the nurse's warm Turkish towels. They'd wrap up my arm in the towels for about twenty minutes, and if that didn't work they'd take me to the sink and run warm water over my arm for ten minutes. Success at last. My veins were bulging.

I added to my Chemo Kit: More strength, a nurse doll named Carole that my daughters gave me for luck, flashy sneaker socks, a trashy romance novel, my Ipod with 2000 songs (gee, I hope this infusion doesn't last that long!), dark chocolate candy bars, and potato chips.

The infusion nurse arrived decked out in a protective gown and wearing rubber gloves. Bells and whistles were going off in my head. I couldn't believe what I was seeing.

The nurse said that they have to be very careful. If this red stuff in the three mega-sized syringes got on their skin, they'd get burned. If it got on the floor tile, it would eat a hole in it.

What's wrong with this picture?

"You mean *that's* going to be injected into me?" I asked. *"Don't I get a protective gown and rubber gloves?"*

"No," the nurse said. She explained that the protective covering wouldn't help me because the red stuff was going in my veins.

Oh, really?

After three seemingly endless hours, the infusion was over, but my arm would hurt for the next two days. I was pooped, not from the infusion, but from the turmoil that surrounded me before it. Whew! Now my instructions were to drink plenty of water and hydrate, hydrate, hydrate.

Ya know, I actually felt like superwoman, and glowed, after my first infusion. I felt marvelous, Dahling.

If I were a drinking person, I would have asked my husband to stop at the first liquor store we came to on the way home and buy me a quart of anything.

Okay, one infusion down, and three to go.

After my first infusion, I dreamed I was levitating. Call Houdini.

After the second infusion, I had a very bad dream, woke myself up and stayed up all night and cried.

After the third infusion, I only wanted to go to the cemetery to visit my wonderful mother-in-law's grave. Does this tell you something?

And after the fourth infusion, chemo brain began to kick in, so I don't remember a thing.

FUZZY FOLLICLES

Driving home from a treatment, the Department of Transportation's road sign said it all: *Squeeze Left.*

"Didn't that just happen?" I said to my husband. I thought those guys just fix roads and hold up traffic.

Arriving home the day of my second infusion, my hair was whipping off my head faster then a speeding bullet. I ran into the house, I grabbed the scissors, the electric trimmer, and a mirror, and said to my husband and daughter, "Let's get down to business."

The three of us went into the backyard. I cut my hair short, my husband shaved my head, and my daughter held the mirror.

We made a great team.

We laughed. What a sight. But, looking in the mirror, I didn't think I had an ugly head, afterall. Actually, my bald head was pretty decent looking for a bald head.

Time to get the wild and crazy baseball caps and funky earrings. I'd wear them until my hair grew back.

But, in case I had to go to some kind of party, I decided I'd need a wig as a backup.

WIGGIN' OUT

I went to the wiggy shop with my best girlfriends, and we laughed our butts off from the minute we stepped into the shop. We explained to the shop owner that it was us we were laughing at, not her shop.

I tried on everything: long hair, short hair, curly hair, you name it.

A redhead? Not.

Maybe blonds have more fun. Not.

Brunette? Forget it, too dark for my gorgeous porcelain skin.

Black hair? No way. I looked like Morticia.

We laughed until our sides split. We took funny, crazy pictures for posterity. I even sent a set to my surgeon. My girlfriends told me I had a beautifully shaped head. What else could they say?

Seeing my reflection in the mirrors with a wig on was crazy. Wigs? Forget it. Just couldn't do it. Wasn't me.

The chemo hats would only be okay if we had 365 days of winter. The scarves called for experts in scarf twirling.

The baseball caps would keep my hair follicles warm. I had hats in red, white and black with silver sequins, several designs of Life is Good, a hat that said "Laugh," and even a hat that said "Cutie."

I wondered if my hair would grow in straight or curly.

I did leave the wiggy shop with a wig just in case an occasion would call for one. But, when I got home, I threw the wig and its mannequin into my closet so I wouldn't have to look at it.

Oh, the hell with all of it. And I watched as my hair grew, s..l..o..w..l..y and curly. My doctor said, "Okay, Eileen, take off the hat and let's see what's going on."

Fuzzy fur.

Bald is beautiful. I wore earrings, makeup, and lipstick and smiled. I was vertical and very happy.

Neon Lights

"Let's pretend you're taking a ride on the Starship Galactica!"

I was lying on my back on a very hard X-ray table and not allowed to move for about an hour. This was so the technicians could do a simulation. In lay terms, they set the formula for my daily radiation therapy so they wouldn't have to re-calculate the formula every day. Thank G-d.

A sneaky technician came up beside me while I was being simulated and injected under the skin of my gorgeous body, tiny, tiny blue ink tattoo dots. This was so they could line up the "big gun" each day to "shoot" at the same spot where the uninvited guest had co-habitated with me.

Damn. And after I'd vowed early on in my life that I'd never, ever get tattoos!

I was told not to worry, that the projected radiation area

would only clip one of my ribs, and was only aimed at a small piece of my right lung.

So, after 10 of 32 of these joyous sessions, I had a sexy sunburn on my right breast and some disgusting fluid-filled blisters, but any little piece of the party-crasher that hadn't been killed before by the red liquid jello was now smoked.

Well, now I could be a connect-the-dot puzzle or a constellation, maybe The Big Dipper. A girlfriend had just gone through simulation, and we decided that she could be The Little Dipper. We howled with laughter.

We also decided that with all our "sisters" who had been simulated for radiation therapy for breast cancer, we could all probably make up The Milky Way.

UH-OH...

During the time of my radiation treatments, I was in bed resting and, as usual, I was religiously checking for foreign objects in my boobs. I couldn't let my guard down for a nanosecond.

Boy, did that pay off! Unbelievably, I found another uninvited guest in my good breast. The little bugger was nowhere near where I would've expected to find one. It was way up high, close to my breast bone and between two ribs. Such a lucky day, you can't imagine.

I said out loud, "What the hell is going on here?"

Very calmly, I called my surgeon and told him that I'd found another party-crasher, and that this one was in my good boob.

The very next day, after a mammogram, an MRI, and a biopsy (ouch), the hard-to-find party-crasher was finally exposed.

When the doctor doing the biopsy finally found the uninvited guest after searching with a very big needle stuck in my chest for about 15 minutes, she said to me, "Don't move."

Doctor you've got to be kidding. Me, move? I don't think so. I was already the color of a sunset from all that poking around. What are the odds? One invader in June and the second in November.

When I arrived home, I phoned all my girlfriends to take a Boob Survey. What should I do? Each one of them first said, "Oh, my G-d." The survey results were unanimous: Remove both boobs and rebuild.

I met with my handsome surgeon and said, "Take these breasts, they're yours."

It was not a difficult decision for me. My husband said, "I don't care what you have or don't have, I only want you."

Love springs eternal.

I did not want to spend the rest of my life soaping up my boobs and wondering where the next uninvited guest was going to pop up.

Thank G-d, all our friends are like sisters and brothers to us. Whenever one of our brothers called, I'd invite him to come over for a big hug and to have their last real feel. I had the guys lined up. What a hoot! Man, I was one popular chick!

And this is the way I handled it, with laughter all the way through.

My surgeon said, "You'll feel as if you've been hit by a truck."

But getting hit by a truck is much better than having more party-crashers roaming around in my boobs. I didn't want to take any chances by saving the boobs. I wanted the cancer as far away from me as possible.

I would have a bilateral mastectomy, and because I'd be having reconstruction, they'd do the skin sparing (ouch) for the foundation of the new boobs. Radiation treatments were halted so my skin would remain soft, creamy, and lovely. I scheduled the surgery, happy because I knew I had the "breast of the breast" surgeons on the job.

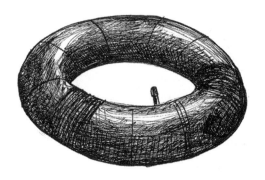

THE GET WELL ENTOURAGE

My wonderful, kind, and thank you, G-d, handsome plastic surgeon…How did I get so lucky with all these handsome doctors? Yahoo! My guardian angel sure knew how to help me keep the pain down.

I met with my plastic surgeon on several occasions. Before he would agree to reconstruct this gorgeous creature (me), he had to explain what was actually going to take place. I had the golden opportunity to look at many beautiful redone breasts in a Breast Album.

The plan: Immediately after one handsome surgeon removed my beautiful breasts, the handsome plastic surgeon would operate and place a blow-up inner tube in each of the empty places where my beauteous breasts had been. Could hurt!

These inner tubes would be filled with fluid: adding a teensy, weensy bit periodically over the course of the next eight months…more pain…until the inner tubes reached the perfect size I wanted to be. How exciting! At that time, the inner tubes would be removed and my plastic surgeon would place two saline balloons in their place.

But the inner tubes felt as if I had a bullet-proof vest on and I was ready to go out with a SWAT team.

Laughing at all this was the way I handled all the crap I had to go through. What could be funnier then wearing two bouncing water balloons?

And then just think, the opportunity of having skin removed from a very touchy place on my body to create new areolas. Then I would have to have the new areolas tattooed for color. It doesn't end there. My new nipples would then be stitched in the center of the tattooed area! Oh, my G-d!

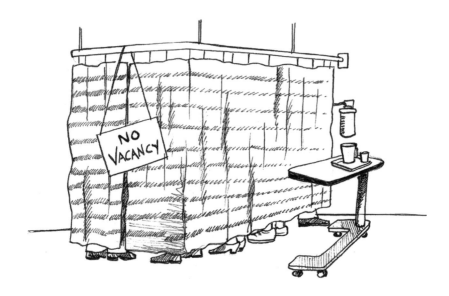

MY PRE-OP CIRCUS

Many of us know what the pre-op cubicles look like with all the apparatus to keep us alive, thank goodness, and a metal standing screen with taut sheets as dividers.

I had quite the cast of characters in my pre-op cubicle:

First, there was me, the patient, ready for my bilateral mastectomy, sitting on a gurney with my johnnie gown untied in the front. A curse on those gowns. I had placed purple and pink sticky hearts all over my body as a reminder to my dear doctor that, "I am allergic to the iodine wash!"

Pinned to my johnnie gown was my tape recorder with

instructions to the anesthesiologist about how to plug in my tape recorder so I could listen to my healing tape while I was in outer space for five and one-half hours.

My darling husband was in the cubicle, along with the head of anesthesiology (I don't know why), a young anesthesiologist (plugging me in), the pre-op nurse, my handsome breast cancer surgeon and the Rabbi Chaplain…all stuffed into the cubicle like sardines.

As the chaplain held my hand and my husband's hand, she began to chant prayers and blessings in Hebrew. This was a new scene for a pre-op cubicle.

Then, suddenly, from under one of the taut sheet cubicle dividers, up popped my gorgeous plastic surgeon. He was waving a large, black magic marker and said that there was no damn room for him in the cubicle so he had to enter from under the curtains. He opened my already opened johnnie gown, and with his big, black marker swished three long dashes down the middle of my chest and several dashes under each of my breasts. I had never been measured for a bra by this method.

It was a zany pre-op stage show. I wish I had a video of it.

The last thing I remember was the OR nurse asking me if the pillow was comfortable under my knees…*Good Night*!

My Post-Op Madness

At 6:00 a.m. the morning after my surgery, a shocking wave of lights sprang to life over my hospital room.

My eyes popped open and I jumped a foot high off the bed. Hard to do when you're all hooked up and you're in la-la land from a morphine drip, but I managed.

What the hell is going on? Standing at the foot of my bed was a group of short people all dressed in white coats. I'm morphed out of my brain.

A very young, brash person introduced himself as a second year resident. He acted like a Little King Tut and said, "We're going to have you up and out of here by the end of the day."

I thought, "Oh really, you think so, wise guy? I guess this is what they call a drive by mastectomy!"

Little King Tut was very lucky this mama was loaded with morphine.

All I could get out of my mouth was, "I don't think so!" My brain really wanted to say, "Little King Tut, pretend I'm your mother."

I pleadingly requested that my surgeon keep The Little King away from me. He needed a course in Bedside Manner 101 and probably a good crack in the head.

I never saw The Little King again, just a lovely, young, angelic female resident who would come in to see if I had enough meds to keep the pain away.

Yes, I really felt as if I'd been hit by a truck. But on a positive note, the dump truck carried the uninvited guests away from my body.

The expanders that had been inserted during the surgery to prepare for the eventual reconstruction were killing me. I felt like I was wearing a bullet proof vest. Also, I had swellings the size of balloons under each arm. What the hell were they? Then I found out. With lymph nodes removed, fluid builds and builds. Lymphedema!

Finally, all the plugs were out of my body except four drains that were still attached to me as take-home party favors. The long rubber hoses with bulbs on the ends were attached to my body by black sewing thread and were going to swing from my body until they were ready to come out.

Two days later, after a couple of pain meds, I was wheeled genteelly down to the pick-up discharge areas.

My husband drove. All the way home, I gently clutched my pillow to my chest under the seatbelt. I only wanted french fries. Other than getting the french fries at a fast food place, I only remember arriving home and falling into our bed, on my back, of course. Morphine is a very good thing to keep you from remembering.

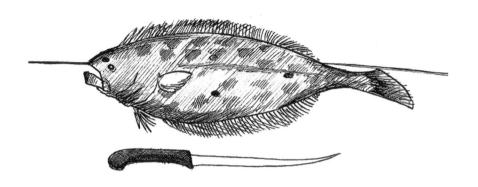

Home Sweet Home

Just call me Linus. My blanket and pillow were with me day and night. My husband never had a problem finding me in the house. There I was, with my blanket and pillow, reclined on anything that would accept my body.

Part of my get well get up was a lovely white vest with Velcro closures. The vest had four inside pouches to hold the drain balloons so they wouldn't dangle by their rubber hoses. This couture would have made a clothing designer flip.

And with two missing boobs and the skin-sparing for reconstruction, my boobless chest looked like two big cinnabuns. It was certainly not romantic. However, my husband and I laughed and decided to have a date at least twice a day. We met in the bathroom, with an Output Chart designed by my teacher husband, and measuring cups, in order to measure the output of the four drains dangling from my battered body.

For three weeks, we diligently measured and kept track. The output had to be under a certain amount before the damn things could be removed. I had one hold-out. Drain number four took an extra week.

Finally, I was ready for the drains to be snapped out. I quickly called the hospital to make an appointment. My oncologist said to me with a little trepidation, "Take a pain pill an hour before you get here!" Oh, great!

I was finally relieved of the four appendages, and we merrily traveled home to follow the continued cleansing instructions for the two big cinnabuns.

Ever feel like a flounder? One incision was being stubborn and not healing well, so I went to see my handsome plastic surgeon, who said, "I have to fix this!"

And, in five seconds, out came the knives, the needles, the thread, and scissors to fix the boo-boo. I went home to continue to heal…Yippee.

More recovery at home. My husband was a fabulous nurse. My family and friends buzzed around me like bees.

My docs cleared me to take a cruise vacation. On the ship, when I was in my bathing suit, some women were staring at my flat chest. I figured they probably felt sorry for me so I gave them two thumbs up.

On my vacation I had lots of time to relax and decide which position was the best for sleep.

Reconstruction? Fuhgeddaboudit!

Four months after my bilateral mastectomy and foundation for reconstruction, and having had lots of time to think, I decided that the expanders that had been placed in my delicate, gorgeous body to save places for my new boobs, were killing me, as in painful.

On a visit with my plastic surgeon, we were casually walking down the hall when he put his arm over my shoulders and said to me, "Well, Eileen, what are we going to do today? Are we going to fill one expander or both?"

"Are you kidding?" I answered, "How about none? Let's take these babies out."

He replied, "I think we have to sit down and have a talk."

And that's what we did.

I told my handsome plastic surgeon that I was a very brave, strong person, but I did not want any more self-induced pain. No new boobs. Instead, I have two wrinkled potholes in my chest surrounded by extra skin. Sounds like a menu. The potholes look like two Shar Pei puppies.

My social worker daughter taught me to look for a positive in every negative. The positives: I don't have to housebreak and walk the puppies or feed the puppies, and I don't have bowls of water on my kitchen floor to trip over.

Now that I think of it, I could have had that handsome plastic surgeon fix my deviated septum, and put a little ski jump at the end of my nose at the same time, do a mini lift to my eyelids, and a little liposuction to slim down my hips.

Nah, I'd had enough surgery.

A date was set for the removal of the inner tubes. I was so happy. I would shop for a breastless wardrobe with new eyeglasses to match.

Instead of hanging out at upscale bra bars, from that point on I would be haunting high-end optical shops. As I write this, I have eight pairs of snazzy prescription glasses. By the time you read this, I'll probably have eight more.

Just when the caterpillar thought the world was over, it became a butterfly.
—proverb

MY PROCLAMATION

I will be flat and sleek for the rest of my life.

I will not wear stuffed bras or fake boobs.

I will never, ever wear bras again. Now I can get rid of the grooves in my shoulders.

I will never have to worry if one boob is high and the other is low.

I will not have to worry about fashionable cleavage anymore.

When we arrived home the day I told my plastic surgeon that I didn't want reconstruction, I ran into the house, grabbed a big garbage bag, and dumped the contents of my bra drawer into it. Then, I ran outside to the trash can and threw the bag away.

Sweet freedom! If it had been the 1960's, I would be braless and right in style. I would have burned my bras instead.

One day, after a shower, I happened to glance at myself in the mirror and saw my battered body. I said out loud, "Eileen, what happened to you?"And then I started to cry. I wondered how I would be able to tuck in my bath sheet. No more cleavage. Well, I guess that's why G-d gave me armpits—so they could hold up my towels. My oncologist had told me, "A moment is okay, but not more than a moment."

If I had any desire to smooth out my puppies, this did not last a long time. My terrific plastic surgeon told me that if he could design the most painful surgery, Shar Pei repair would be it!

FRIED NEURONS

I was really relieved. Science has finally proven that "chemo brain" really exists. Little neurons in my brain had been demolished from the chemo fruit punch infusion. Sometimes the neurons in our brains regenerate, and sometimes they don't.

I forgot my left from my right. I forgot the name of the person I was just talking to, face to face. I would be on the phone and would forget the next word that was in the sentence, and I had to use another word to fill in the blank.

When I went to the basement to get something, I'd go all the way down the stairs, and then forget what I went down for. I would yell up the stairs, "Would someone please tell me why I came down to the basement?"

Thank G-d it was *not* my imagination.

A chemo conversation overheard. One friend to another: "I don't know where I am." The friend replies: "Don't worry, you're here!"

My brain continues to think I have breasts, so when someone drives into our driveway, I run down the hall to put on my bra. But, when I whip open my bra drawer it's empty.

My daughters wait patiently on the phone while I try to remember the great thing that happened that I called to tell them about.

How many times have I heard my husband say, "Eileen, where did you put the checkbook this time?"

So, to retrain my brain, I decided to volunteer at a local library, hoping that the Dewey Decimal System would kick my brain into gear.

Was there an upside to chemo brain? You bet. I forgot how to cook!

THE BEAST

My poor little lymphatic system became so confused after my breasts were removed. The lymphatic system under my arms had been cut during surgery so the natural flow of my lymphatic fluid had no where to run and no where to hide. That caused a major backup.

The backup gave me two water balloons, one in front of each of my armpits. I called my favorite Aunt Lil, who had been so marvelous helping me with her outrageous humor during my cancer siege that I asked if I could name my lymphatic fluid condition after her.

The Lillies, my lymphedema, became permanent little balloons in front of my armpits.

I went to a Lymphedema Drainage Massage (LDM) therapist who works at getting The Lillies to take new routes and flow into other parts of my body.

The lymphatic fluid can't be withdrawn by a needle, thank G-d. It must be gently coaxed to move by itself. This meant I had to learn exercises to hand pump and massage my body to redirect the flow.

After more then 40 hours of hand pump training, The Lillies finally began to get into the flow of things. My balloons need constant attention, so I pump them by diligently doing weird and funky exercises to my body twice a day to keep the flow moving.

My Lillies have a mind of their own. They don't like salty food. They don't like diet soda. And no matter how diligently I pump my arms when I walk, no matter how much I talk to them, knead and massage them, and tell them I love them but it's time to leave me already, The Lillies persist, so I keep on massaging and pumping.

I researched and researched. I located a therapist certified in another fluid moving method called The Chikly Method, named after its creator, Dr. Chikly. The therapist manually mapped my lymph system, a very spooky thing to watch, to feel which way it was flowing, and attempted to teach the stubborn Lillies once and for all which way is down.

All I wanted to accomplish was pushing these balloons out of my armpits. So, I wore a compression shirt, which helps to keep The Lillies in constant motion. At last, something positive: The compression shirt does double duty as a girdle. Yes! Another bonus is I can't eat as much because the pressure from the shirt reduced my appetite so I've lost weight. Right on.

The Lillies are smaller now, I know how to pump and massage my body, I look sleeker wearing a compression shirt, and I have lost weight.

The new method seemed to be working for a while, but wasn't good enough for me, so I continued researching and found another new method. The Vodder Method, and the most talented physical therapists I've ever met in my life. The Vodder Method, which is a manual method, goes down layer by layer, into your body and helps to take out scar tissue, bone bruises, and locked-up connective tissue, and now The Lillies are beginning to empty a little by themselves. A miracle.

I still do my wild and crazy exercises, plus some new cuties. This method is working. I am in charge. I am winning the war of the lymphedema balloons.

I'm also trying gluten-free foods, since I'm told that the gluten in foods prohibits the smooth flow of the lymphatic system.

I will do anything I have to in order to win this War of the Water Balloons, and I am winning.

DEAR HENRY!

In 1972, I created a stationery business, and working out of my home I sold wedding invitations and accessories to brides-to-be.

Over the phone, I met a young man with a great voice who worked in the accounting department of one of the companies I did business with. Our friendship, by phone, continued through the years. As my business grew, and Henry accepted promotions from one company to another, we still had never personally met. For years, we told each other jokes and laughed at crazy things going on in the stationery business, all by phone.

I baked Henry pepperoni breads as Christmas gifts, year after year, for 36 years.

Although I'd closed my successful stationery business in 1992, my friend Henry and I continued to talk and laugh on the phone with the blessing of our spouses.

In 2005, I called him to tell him I had just been diagnosed with breast cancer. He was upset to tears. But, as always, we laughed over silly stuff!

One day, in 2008, we were on the phone and decided after this wild phone friendship of 36 years, it was time to meet in person.

Finally, we set the big date. Not only had we never met, we'd never even seen photos of each other.

So it was pretty funny, when before The Big Date, Henry said, "Eileen, you probably won't recognize me. I'm short, bald, and older than when we first met."

"Henry, don't worry about it," I said. "You won't recognize me either. I have gray hair and no breasts!"

We met with our spouses at a commuter lot off the highway. We had described our cars to each other. We got there first so they'd easily find us. I spotted Henry's car as soon as it pulled in. He parked right next to us. We all got out of our cars, and the four of us hugged and kissed like long lost relatives.

We went out to lunch and then took a long walk. We never stopped laughing. By the time you read this, we will have all spent another day together.

BITS AND PIECES

As a man once said to me after learning I'd had cancer, "There is a "*can*" in cancer."

You may have heard of the phenomenon call Phantom Pain Syndrome. Well, I have Phantom Bra Syndrome. Subconsciously, my mind thinks I'm wearing a bra, so I reach to my sides to pull it down.

Think about this: A mammogram after a biopsy. Ouch!

My birth sign is CANCER! And that sign is represented by the crab. Well, some days I wobble to the left, some days I wobble to the right, some days I walk the center line, and some days I fall on my back, wiggle my claws, and can't get up.

Going into surgery to have her nipples and areolas replaced as part of reconstruction, a friend said she'd glued chocolate kisses on her breasts so that the surgeon would know the exact place she wanted her nipples to be!

After I had my 6 1/2 pounds of breast tissue removed, I had to retrain myself how to walk straight and tall. Roll those shoulders back, pull that tummy in, straighten that back and march onward.

A very Irish girlfriend wanted her surgeon to make her new nipples in the shape of shamrocks. He didn't. The doctor had no sense of humor.

Arriving at the hospital to check in for a minor procedure, I had to be issued a new ID card. The receptionist asked if anything had changed since I'd been there last and I said, "Yes, I no longer have breasts!" She was so surprised she didn't know whether to laugh or cry.

A girlfriend told me that she'd always been told that she looked like her father. After her bilateral mastectomy she joked, "*Now*, I look like my father!"

Shopping while on a restful vacation, I met a beautiful young woman and I noticed she had a very flat chest. We looked at each other and then hugged. My husband and I talked with her and her husband, and they told us that they joked that they had decided that she'd have a bilateral mastectomy because she didn't need her breasts anymore since she'd never made any money with them anyway!

Who would have thought this Jewish girl would've become so familiar with prayer groups, prayer lines, rosary beads, lighting candles in churches, and praying in every church I would happen to pass. I also became very familiar with the Cathedral of Saint Patrick in New York, Our Lady of Lourdes of France, and Our Lady of Fatima in Portugal. I was being prayed for around the world. I even called on St. Anthony to intervene for me a few times. All this has been taught to me by my wonderfully spiritual Catholic girlfriends.

Making a lunch date with a friend, I told her I could not make it on a particular day because I had an appointment with my gynecologist for my yearly checkup. My friend retorted,

"Why the hell are you going for a GYN checkup? You've had a total hysterectomy and now you have no boobs!" I replied with dignity, "I still have a vagina!"

A wonderful, devout Catholic friend, I've renamed St. Mary, prayed and prayed for my complete recovery. Every week, she visits convalescent homes to cheer the residents, so she corralled all her buddies there and asked them to, "Get on their "beads," get into their rocking chairs, and start praying for me."

Months later, when she knew I had a good prognosis, she corralled her buddies again, asked them to, "Get on their "beads," get back into their rocking chairs, and thank G-d for my recovery."

If there's a 2-3% chance of something going wrong or being unusual, my longtime friend falls into that small percentage. She was a nurse/health educator teaching women to do breast self-exams. She found a lump in her lymphnodes. The lump never showed up in repeat mammograms. In fact, when she had her mastectomy, the surgeon, who had no sense of humor at all, came into her hospital room and told her that the pathologist couldn't find the lump in the breast itself. With a straight face, she asked if she could have her breast back. The surgeon looked at her with horror, and said her breast was in frozen pieces! "I know that." she replied. "Afterall, I'm a nurse, but since there's no pathology showing in my breast, which has been removed, maybe I could make a puzzle out of the pieces?"

P.S. And yes, only 2-3% of patients have no discernable lump!

The top of my bathing suit is a bunch of ruffles. I'd never worn ruffles in my life. Prior to my surgery the only ruffles I'd ever liked were in a bag, very crunchy, and could be purchased at any market.

Remember to laugh…and love life with all your heart.

This is Not the End

"Once Upon A Time" stories usually end with "Happily Ever After!"

Laughter has carried me through some really difficult times. When someone looks at my flat chest when I'm out in public, I just look back with a smile and usually make the other person smile, too.

I try to find humor in everything. I do my best to have a good laugh at least once a day, and it doesn't matter what it's about. I have always had a quick wit, and I use it all the time.

A very dear friend gave me a little plaque that read, "Keep looking up, that is where miracles come from."

So, every day I look up at the magnificent sky, and I'm thankful for waking up healthy that day.

I let stress go over my head.

I put everyone in my prayers who has health issues.

I thank G-d every day for my wonderful family and our friends who carried me and my family through this trying time. Friends near and far, and prayers from all religions, have made my daily life very peaceful knowing how much friends and strangers cared.

I'm thankful to my dedicated medical team, whose skill and knowledge helped me get well. I kept them laughing along the way, and they insisted that I write this book, and encouraged me every step of the way.

If this book can bring a smile to someone who's having a bad day from breast cancer, it will make me very happy.

Having cancer has changed my life. I am still the same Eileen, but my outlook on life, how I approach things, how I handle situations, happy or sad, has taken on new dimensions.

The list of breast cancer survivors gets longer and longer as improved treatments and medications emerge.

But, what's most important is AWARENESS. Check your boobs carefully every month. You'll never regret it.

I've written this book with admiration and love to all my "sisters" who have walked this same path.

Always remember that *Laughter Is The Breast Medicine!*

Thank You and Hugs To...

My husband Arney and our two fabulous daughters, Marcy and Dana, our son-in-law, Mike, and our grandson, Michael for all their love, support, inspiration, and laughter.

My mom, my sister, Bev, my brother-in-law, Bill and my nephew, Michael, for their love, support and strength.

Our priceless friends and extended family, who kept us afloat with their prayers, phone calls, visits and support.

Everyone who surrounded me while I recovered and became strong again, including Amy Dunion, Carol Gordon and Joe Coppa, Laura Carramore, Herta Payson, and my wonderful survivors support group at Backus Hospital in Norwich, CT.

Linda Cutone, a very special friend, who was sent to me by my guardian angel.

My medical team: Drs. Mehra Golshan, Charles Hergrueter, and Suzanne Berlin at Dana Farber Cancer Institute and Brigham and Women's Hospital, Boston, MA.

Dr. Ann Semolic, my PCP, and her staff, Willimantic, CT, and the staff of the radiation treatment center at Backus Hospital, Norwich, CT, who were all magnificent.

My publishing team: My editor, Nina L. Diamond, who also taught me all about publishing; Kraig Sanquedolce, for his brilliant illustrations; Shoshanah Siegel, my talented graphic artist and book designer; John (J.P.)Pickering, my website designer, who also taught me computer literacy; Stuart Bryant, IM Technology, my computer specialist; Andrew Gordon, my printer representative from Sheridan Books who has been terrific; Joe Matera, who has graciously given me warehouse space for book storage; and my friend of 40 years, Johanne Philbrick, Ph.D, whose expertise in the English language is extraordinary.

And last but not least, my buddy, Rich Alexander, who continues to tell me that I should never have been allowed to own a computer.

How to Find Me

To Get In Touch With Eileen...

you can...

Email her at eyekap@att.net

or

to order additional copies of "Laughter,"

go to her website laughteristhebreastmedicine.com.

FOR YOUR THOUGHTS

ABOUT THE AUTHOR

W hen Eileen Kaplan was routinely doing her monthly breast self-exam in June, 2005, she discovered a tumor in her right breast. After going through a lumpectomy, chemotherapy, and radiation, she discovered a tumor in her left breast. Eileen decided to have a bilateral mastectomy.

She has been an award-winning Realtor, an X-ray technologist, an assistant on the staff of Connecticut's Department of Children & Families Special Review Unit, and for 20 years ran her own invitations and fine stationery business. In 2009, she was named Salem Free Public Library's Volunteer of the Year.

Eileen is a Breast Cancer Awareness Advocate and she mentors women who are dealing with health and physical issues associated with breast cancer and its aftermath. She is very active with her Breast Cancer Survivors Support Group at Backus Hospital in Norwich, CT. Reading and knitting are two of her favorite pastimes.

How ironic it is that, prior to Eileen's cancer diagnosis, she was an active volunteer raising funds for cancer research. The year before her diagnosis she was awarded "The 2004 Daffodil Days Award" by the American Cancer Society for her successful

Daffodil Sales Campaign, never thinking that the money she had raised would possibly be used towards her own treatment.

She lives in Southeastern Connecticut with her husband, Arney. They have two daughters, Marcy and Dana, Dana's husband Mike and a grandson, Michael.

When Eileen was diagnosed and successfully treated for breast cancer, she discovered that laughter is the breast medicine.